Capricorn

Astrology Coloring Book

Color Your Zodiac Sign

The 12 Signs

Sign Symbols

ARIES

TAURUS

GEMINI

CANCER

LEO

VIRGO

LIBRA

SCORPIO

SAGITTARIUS

CAPRICORN

AQUARIUS

PISCES

Capricorn

December 22 - January 19

THE LAST TRIO OF THE Earth signs is Capricorn. Like other Earth signs, they are practical and grounded. Their ruling planet of Saturn represents hard work and determination, and this manifests through their incredible self-control and responsibility. Because of this same quality they are often seen as stiff and uncompromising to others. They are brave and tenacious and once they set their mind to something nothing will stop them from getting it done.

Symbol: Goat

Planet: Saturn

Element: Earth

Colors: Brown, Black

Traits: Disciplined, Responsible, Hardworking, Unforgiving, Condescending

Constellation:

CAPRICORN

CAPRICORN

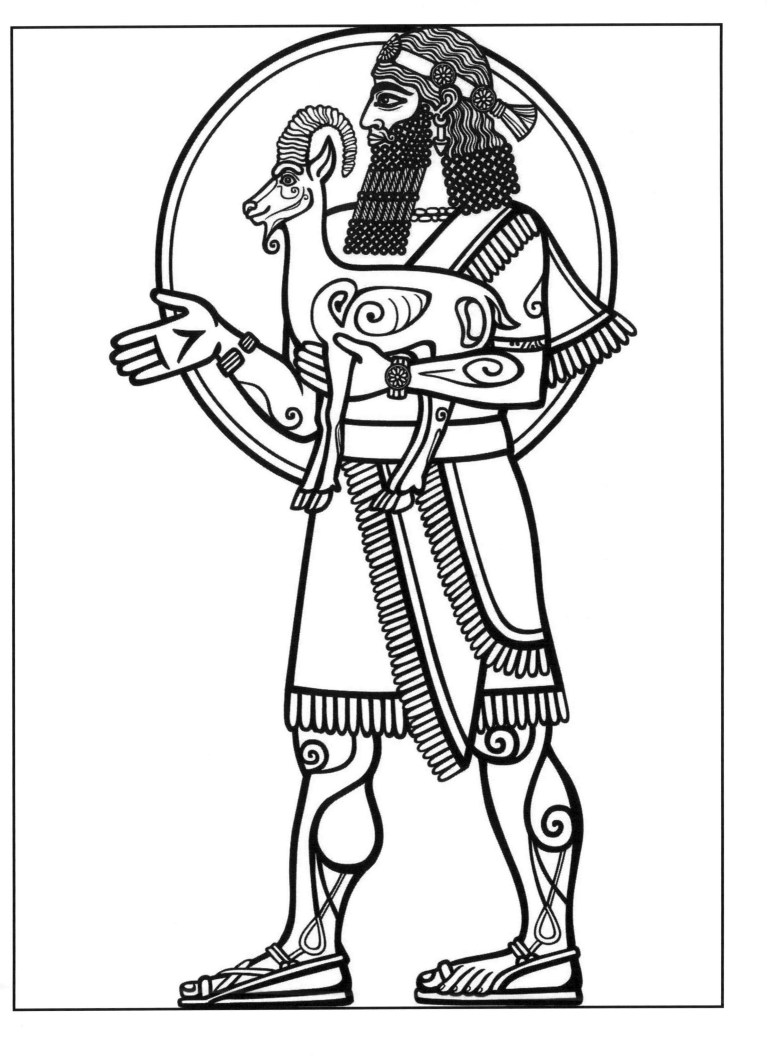

CAP ℞iCORN

Capricorn

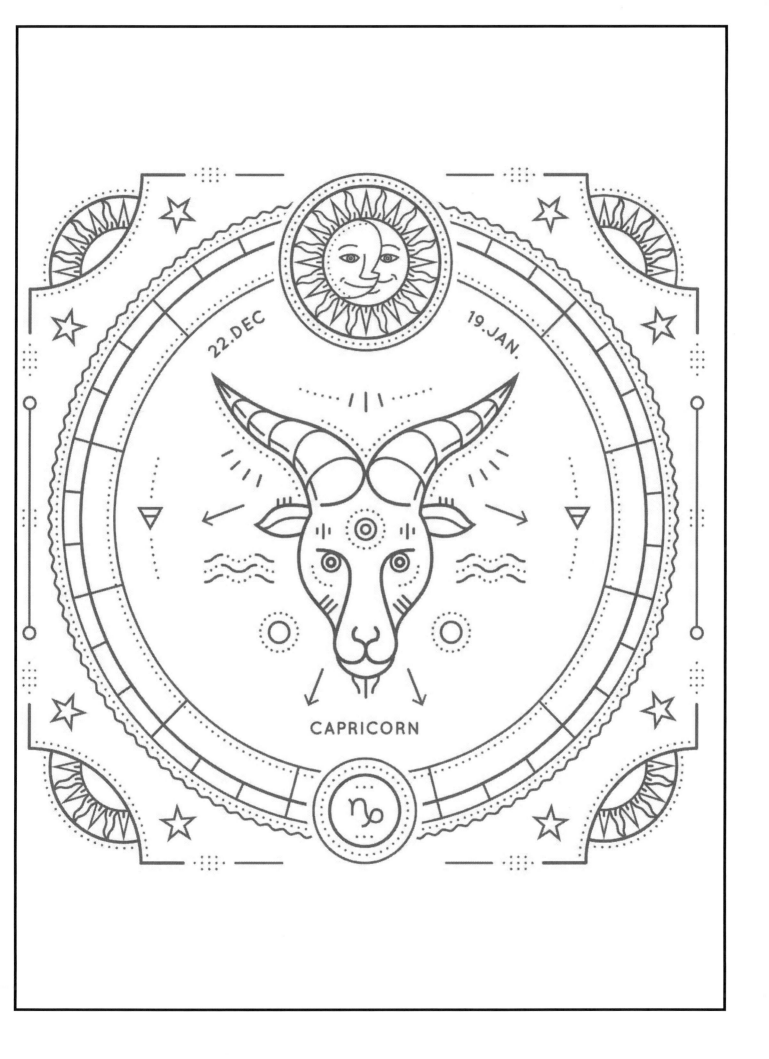

Capricorn

♑ Capricorn

Made in the USA
Las Vegas, NV
30 December 2020